YOU'RE THE VO

Alicia Keys

	In the Book	On the CD
very Little Bit Hurts	4	Track 1
allin'	12	Track 2
irlfriend	18	Track 3
I Ain't Got You	24	Track 4
o One	30	Track 5
arma	36	Track 6
perwoman	43	Track 7
enage Love Affair	52	Track 8
Woman's Worth	59	Track 9
ou Don't Know My Name	66	Track 10

© 2008 by International Music Publications Ltd
First published by International Music Publications Ltd in 2008
International Music Publications Ltd is a Faber Music company
3 Queen Square, London WC1N 3AU

Edited by Lucy Holliday
Backing tracks arranged by Danny G
Backing vocals by Kathryn Knight

Photograph © Salifu Idriss/Redferns

Printed in England by Caligraving Ltd

ISBN10: 0-571-53234-9
EAN13: 978-0-571-53234-6

To buy Faber Music publications or to find out about the full range of titles available,
please contact your local music retailer or Faber Music sales enquiries:

Faber Music Ltd, Burnt Mill, Elizabeth Way, Harlow, CM20 2HX England
Tel: +44(0)1279 82 89 82
Fax: +44(0)1279 82 89 83
sales@fabermusic.com fabermusic.com

Alicia Keys
25 January 1981

Alicia Keys is one of the most successful American R&B singer songwriters, selling over 20 million albums worldwide, and winning numerous awards for her achievements in music.

Born Alicia J. Augello-Cook in Harlem, New York in 1981, Keys was introduced to the entertainment industry at an early age, starring in 1985 in an episode of the hugely popular U.S. comedy programme, *The Cosby Show*. At the age of seven, she began to learn classical piano, and started writing songs four years later. Keys was then accepted into the prestigious Professional Performance Arts School, in Manhattan, which helped to develop her vocal skills, as well as continuing with her piano playing. At sixteen she graduated as the class valedictorian (the highest ranked student).

Then followed an opportunity to go to Columbia University, where Keys enrolled as a student, but dropped out early on to concentrate exclusively on her music career. Assuming the stage name, Alicia Keys, she signed a demo deal with So So Def, a label distributed by Columbia Records, and co-wrote and recorded a song called 'Dah Dee Dah (Sexy Thing)' which appeared on the soundtrack to the 1997 blockbuster, *Men In Black*. Although the song was Keys' first professional recording, it was never released as a single, and caused disputes between her and her record label, so her contract with them ended quickly.

After the Columbia deal ended, Keys met Clive Davis, then the president of Arista Records, who signed her up, only for her career to stall when Davis was ousted from the company in 2000. Keys then followed Davis to his newly formed J Records label, and recorded the songs 'Rock Wit U' and 'Rear View Mirror', featuring on the soundtracks to the films *Shaft* and *Dr Dolittle 2* respectively. An aggressive publicity campaign followed, and her debut album *Songs In A Minor* was released in June 2001, entering at the top of the charts.

Songs In A Minor was a huge success for Keys, selling over ten million units worldwide, and as a result she became the best selling new artist of 2001. The album won five Grammys, and platinum certificates in ten different countries. 'Fallin', the first single from the album, was a worldwide hit, and remained at the top of the Billboard Charts for six weeks.

In 2003 Keys released her second album, *The Diary Of Alicia Keys*, which again was a huge success, debuted at number 1 in the US, and spawned the hit singles 'You Don't Know My Name' and 'If I Ain't Got You'. 2005 saw the release of her first live album, recorded as part of the MTV Unplugged series, and giving Keys her third number 1 record, being the first Unplugged by a female artist to reach number one.

Acting was on the agenda in 2007, and Keys made her big-screen debut in the film *Smokin' Aces*, then following it up by starring in *The Nanny Diaries*, before releasing her third studio album *As I Am* in November, giving Keys her fourth consecutive number one album.

In 2008, Keys and Jack White (of the White Stripes) recorded the theme song to *Quantum Of Solace*, the 22nd James Bond film. The song, 'Another Way To Die' was written by White, and was the first duet in the history of Bond soundtracks. Keys is also continuing with her acting career, starring alongside Jennifer Hudson in *The Secret Life Of Bees*, and also playing a child prodigy pianist in the forthcoming film *Compassion In Black And White*.

As well as being a musician and actress, Keys is also Global Ambassador for Keep A Child Alive, a charity that helps African children obtain medicine for AIDS. She is also a spokeswoman for Frum Tha Ground Up, an organisation set up to inspire and motivate American kids to achieve success on all levels.

backing track 1

EVERY LITTLE BITS HURTS

Words and Music by Edward Cobb

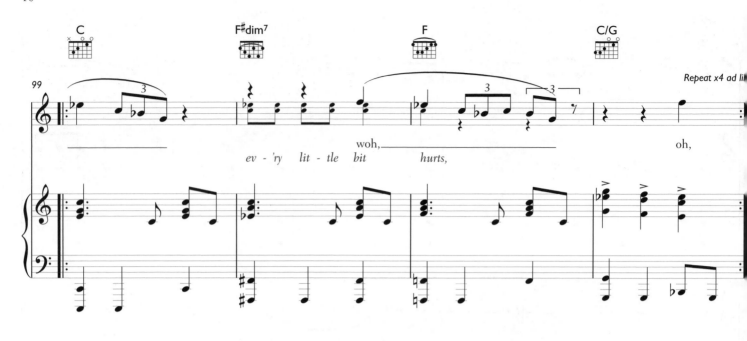

backing track [2]

FALLIN'

Words and Music by Alicia Augello-Cook

14

backing track 3

GIRLFRIEND

Words and Music by Alicia Augello-Cook, Jermaine Dupri, Joshua Thompson,
Robert Diggs, Russell Jones and Derrick Harris

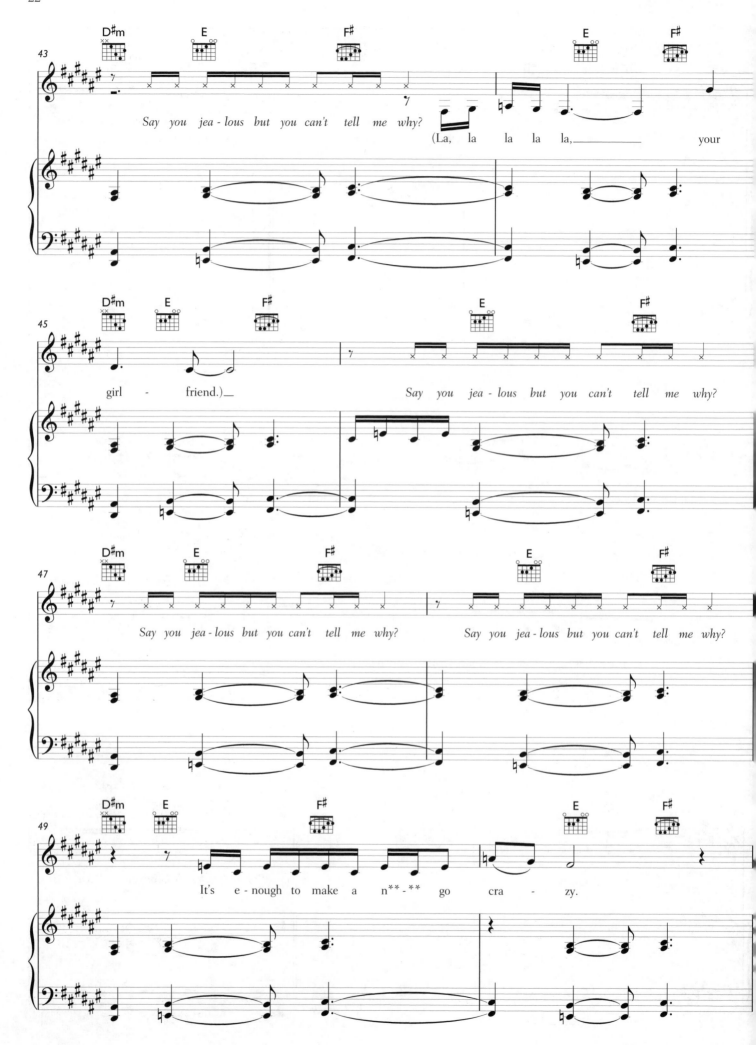

1.
2.
E
F♯
N.C.
D♯m
E
F♯
of you.
Oh, oh.)
I think I'm jea - lous of your
Oh, oh,
N.C.
girl - friend, al - though she's just a girl that is your friend.
I think I'm jea - lous of your girl - friend, she shares a spe - cial part
E
F♯
of you.
Oh, oh.
Say you jea-lous but you can't tell me why?

IF I AIN'T GOT YOU

Words and Music by Alicia Augello-Cook

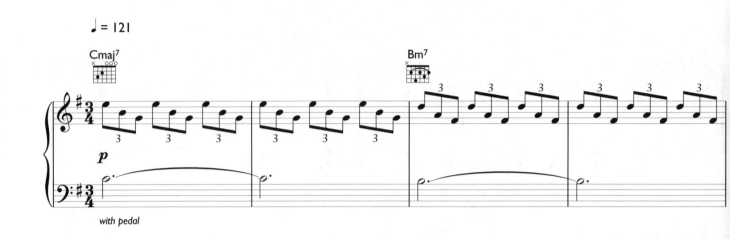

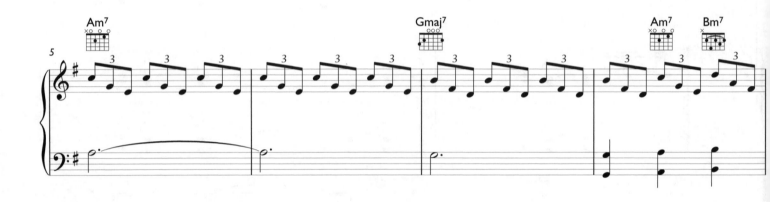

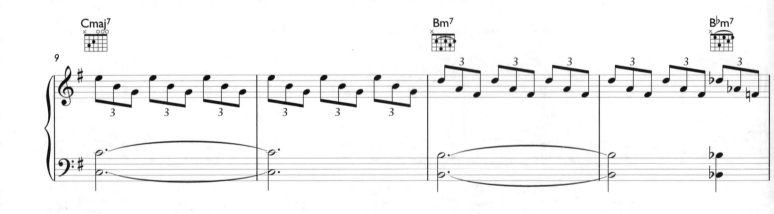

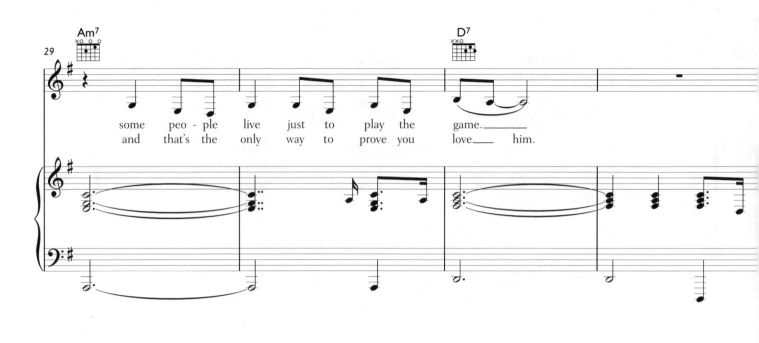

some peo - ple live just to play the game._____
and that's the only way to prove you love___ him.

Some_____ peo - ple think that the phy - si - cal things de -
Hand_____ me the world on a sil - ver plat - ter, and

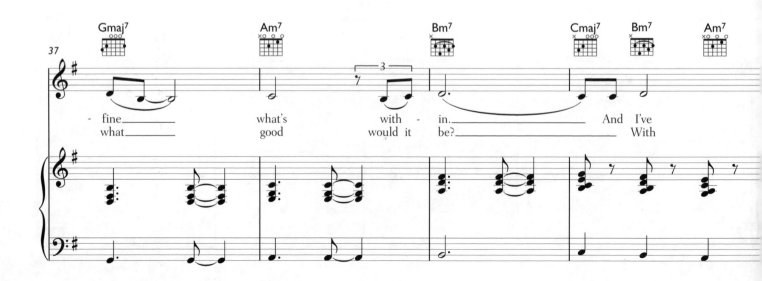

- fine_____ what's with - in._____ And I've
what_____ good would it be?_____ With

28

backing track 5

NO ONE

Words and Music by Alicia Augello-Cook, Kerry Brothers Jr and George Harry

backing track 6

KARMA

Words by Alicia Augello-Cook and Taneisha Smith
Music by Alicia Augello-Cook and Kerry Brothers Jr

1. Weren't you the one who said that you don't want me an-y-more,
2. And when you came home you'd al-ways have some sor-ry ex-cuse,

down.) Now__ who's cry - in',___ de - si - rin'___ to come back__ to me?__

backing track 7

SUPERWOMAN

Words and Music by Alicia Augello-Cook, Linda Perry and Steve Mostyn

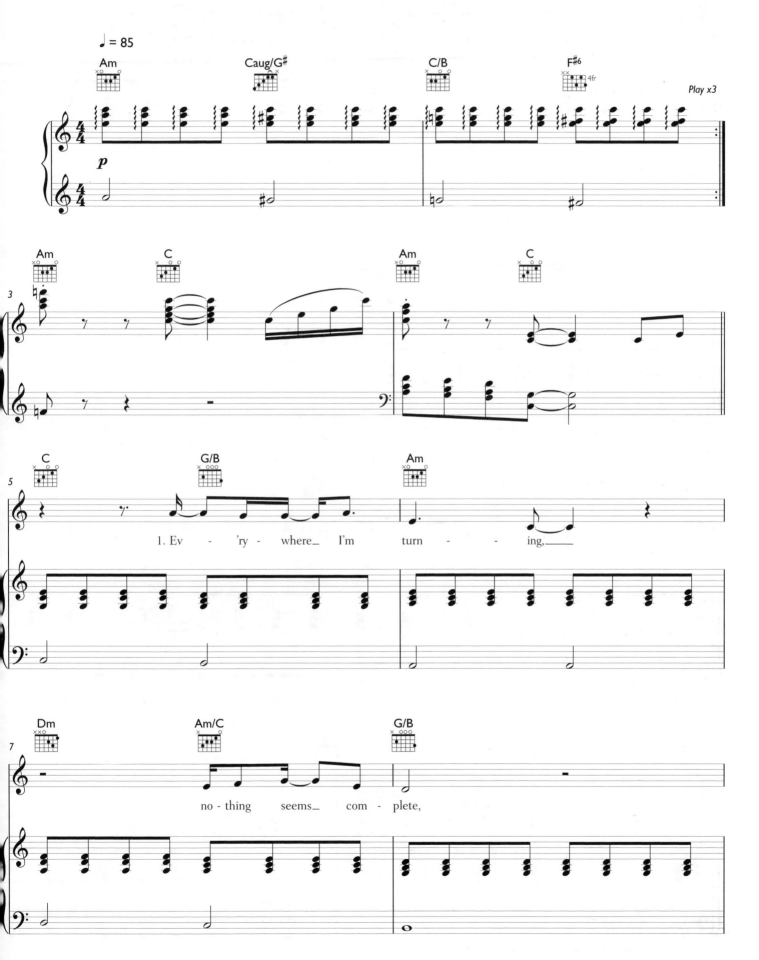

48

50

backing track 8

TEENAGE LOVE AFFAIR

Words and Music by Alicia Augello-Cook, Jack Splash, Harold Lilly,
Carl Hampton, Josephine Bridges, Tom Nixon and Matt Kahane

backing track 9

A WOMAN'S WORTH

Words and Music by Alicia Augello-Cook and Erika Rose

1. You could buy me dia-monds, you could buy me
(2.) fair - ly, I'll give you all

pearls,_____ take me on a cruise a-round_ the world._____ (Ba -
my goods,_____ treat you like a real wom - an should._____ (Ba -

YOU DON'T KNOW MY NAME

Words and Music by Alicia Augello-Cook, Kanye West,
Harold Lilly, Ralph Bailey, Mel Kent and Ken Williams

(Round and round and round we go,)___ ___ name.___ will you e - ver know?___

Spoken: I'm gonna have to just go ahead and call this boy. Hello? Can I speak to, to Michael? Oh, hey, how you doing? I feel kind of silly doing this, but, this is the waitress from the coffeehouse on 39th and Lennox. You know, the one with the braids? Yeah. Well I see you on Wednesday's all the time. You come in every Wednesday, on your lunch break I think, and you always order the special with the hot chocolate. Look man, I mean, I know girls don't usually do this, but I was wondering if maybe we could get together outside the restaurant one day? You know, 'cause I do look a lot different outside my work clothes. Wait, hold on, my cell phone's breaking up, hold on... Can you hear me now? Yeah. So what day did you say? Oh yeah,

Thursday's perfect. It feels___ like